25¢

Weekly Reader Children's Book Club presents

The Little Horse
That Raced a Train

The Little Horse
That Raced a Train

 Little, Brown and Company

with pictures
by WESLEY DENNIS

by WILMA PITCHFORD HAYS

Boston • Toronto

Weekly Reader Children's Book Club Edition

Published simultaneously in Canada
by Little, Brown & Company (Canada) Limited

PRINTED IN THE UNITED STATES OF AMERICA

To Grace Ann

The Little Horse
That Raced a Train

ELMER HORNE stood beside the railroad track and waited for the train to take him to school. He saw the train come from a tunnel down the mountain.

"Whoo-ooo-wooo," shrilled the train whistle.

Elmer thought it was a lonely sound. Elmer was lonely.

Until a few days before, Elmer had had friends to play with. He had waited with other children near a street corner for a yellow school bus.

Then his mother and father and Elmer moved to a construction camp in the Rocky Mountains. His father was helping build a tunnel for the railroad.

Each morning the construction train carried his father and the other men to work. Then it took Elmer up the mountain to a town where there was a school. Each afternoon the train brought Elmer home when it returned with supplies and mail.

"Whoo-ooo-wooo," shrilled the whistle again.

The short train chugged to a stop in front of Elmer. The engineer leaned out the window and grinned. The fireman reached down and helped Elmer climb onto the high platform. "All aboard!" he shouted. The train moved on.

Elmer went into the empty passenger car and sat in a seat by a window. He watched the lonely ranches way, way below in the valley.

The train thundered into the crevice of a high wild

canyon. It was half dark between the strange rock walls. Elmer thought he saw an antelope in a cluster of pine trees. But he couldn't be sure. He heard a howl that sounded like a coyote. He rubbed the shivery tingle at the end of his freckled nose.

Then Elmer saw the little horse. She was grazing on a narrow strip of green grass between the railroad track and the rock wall.

The little horse raised her black head when she heard the train. She snorted and kicked up her black hind hoofs. The little horse was black all over except for her long white mane and her plume of white tail.

When the train reached the horse, she tossed her white mane and began to run. She raced right beside Elmer's window.

The train came out of the wild canyon and sped down a slope. The little black horse laid back her ears and stretched her black legs long. And she kept up with the train. The little horse's head was right beside Elmer's head. There was only the window glass between.

The little horse's eyes gleamed. She whinnied loud and sassy.

Elmer pressed his nose against the glass and shouted, "Come on, come on, we're going to pass you!"

The little horse raced so fast that her long white mane stood out uneven in the wind. Her plume of white tail streamed out behind. She runs like a streak of lightning, Elmer thought. I'll call her Lightning.

"Come on, Lightning," he called. "We're climbing up the mountain again.'

The train climbed higher and higher. Up. Up. Up. And Lightning was right beside it. Then the rail bed along the side of the mountain grew narrow. There was no room for anything but the train, not even for the small horse.

Elmer sat back in his seat in the empty car. He looked at the sky and the mountain. He felt more lonely than ever. Then, quick as a wink, he pressed his nose against the window again.

Lightning was scrambling up the side of the rocky

mountain wall beside them. Her ears were laid back.
She slid and strained to reach the top before the
train did.

She disappeared in a crevice near the rocky top.
But when the train pulled over the divide, there was
Lightning. She stood on a flat boulder high above.
She looked down upon the train.

Elmer laughed.

The little horse watched the engine gather speed again. She kicked up her black hind hoofs. She tossed her white mane. She whinnied loud and sassy as if to say, "I won. I won. Wasn't it fun?"

"She's grinning," Elmer said. "That Lightning is actually grinning."

When Elmer got off the train in the town, he asked the two trainmen if they had seen the little horse race with the train.

"I was too busy watching signals," the fireman said.

The engineer said, "No sensible horse would be up there this time of year. The ranchers took their horses off summer pasture into the safety of the valley a month ago."

"I saw this little black horse," Elmer said again, politely. "She raced with us. She didn't stop until she was on the very top of the mountain."

The engineer grinned and winked at the fireman. "My kids tell things like that sometimes, too," he said. "Guess they want company so they make-believe."

Elmer felt his cheeks grow hot. He didn't say any more about the little horse. He knew what he had seen all right, but he wasn't going to be laughed at.

As he walked to school, he thought about Lightning. In the schoolroom he sketched a horse's head with a long mane that streamed in the wind.

His teacher walked up the aisle and stopped at his desk. "That's very good," she said, "but this is the time to do arithmetic."

Elmer put the picture of the little horse in his desk. Each day for a week the little black horse raced

11

that train to the mountaintop. She always won. The little horse and Elmer became good friends through that train window. Then one morning when Elmer waked, he heard the wind howling. He saw snow falling. He bundled up in his heaviest wool jacket. He wore his red cap with the fur earflaps.

That morning Elmer could hardly see the little black horse as she raced beside the train. The snow was like a white curtain between them. Once Lightning floundered in a drift of snow, half-buried.

Elmer caught his breath. Then Lightning was beside his window again. She ran as hard as ever. And when the train pulled over the divide, there was the little black horse on top of the boulder high above them. Snow swirled around her. But she was there.

It snowed all day and all night. The next day the train could not get up the mountain and Elmer could not go to school. After two days, the construction crew put a snowplow on the front of the engine. It opened the track. Elmer could hardly wait to see Lightning.

All the way through the wild canyon, he pressed his freckled nose against the window of the train and watched. There was snow everywhere, deep, deep snow. It filled all the valleys and crevices. He could not see Lightning anywhere. Surely in all this white snow, a black horse would be easy to find, he thought.

As the engine groaned up the mountain, Elmer's stomach felt sick. He blinked his eyes hard. What had become of the little horse that raced the train? The train climbed to the top of the divide. Elmer swallowed and swallowed. The lump in his throat would not go away.

Then Elmer saw Lightning just where he had seen

14

her last in the snowstorm. The little horse was on the mountaintop. The wind had swept the flat boulder clean of snow. Lightning stood on it. Elmer shouted.

Lightning saw the train. She tossed her mane. She kicked up her hind hoofs. She whinnied loud and sassy. Then she ran from one edge of the boulder to the other. That was as far as she could go. Deep, deep snow covered the mountainsides right up to that boulder.

Lightning has been here these three days, Elmer thought. She can't get off the mountaintop because the snow would cover her if she stepped into it.

Elmer's heart beat hard. Lightning must be hungry. She must be lonely.

Now Elmer didn't care whether the trainmen laughed at him or not. He ran to the engine.

"Look!" he cried. "There is the little horse just as I told you!"

The fireman stopped watching signals and looked out the window. The engineer put on the brake and looked out the window. "Where?" they said.

Elmer pointed. "Up there," he said, "and the snow must be about a mile deep all around her."

The men looked. They let out low, surprised whistles. "There *is* a horse and she's got herself into a real fix," the fireman said.

"The snow isn't a mile deep," the engineer said, "but it surely is too deep for anyone to reach that

horse or for her to get down without help."

Elmer's heart beat hard. The serious look on the men's faces told him that Lightning was in real trouble.

"She's hungry. We have to do something," Elmer said.

"Not a thing we can do now," the engineer said. "We'll have to do some thinking." He started the train and took Elmer on to school.

Elmer could not study. He told his teacher about the little horse on the mountaintop. It was time for arithmetic, but his teacher wanted to help Lightning, too. She let the class talk about what could be done about the little horse.

"The firemen could get up there with a ladder," one boy said, but Elmer shook his head. No ladder would reach that high.

"We should tell the policeman. He always knows what to do," a girl said. But Elmer shook his head. If an engineer and a fireman didn't know what to do, a policeman wouldn't either.

"We could throw corn up there," another boy said. But Elmer shook his head. Not even the best baseball pitcher in the country could throw an ear of corn that far.

"Someone could get up there on snowshoes," a girl suggested, "and he could take some big, big snowshoes to put on Lightning —" But Elmer shook his head. No snowshoes would fit Lightning.

A boy cried, "We could get a big net and hold it. We could coax Lightning to jump into it." Elmer didn't have to shake his head. All the class laughed. They knew that wouldn't work.

"Once, I read about a horse in a newspaper," a girl said. Elmer's heart began to pound.

Nearly everyone read newspapers. If there was anyone, anywhere, who could help Lightning, the newspaper might find him. Elmer was so excited he stood right up on his feet. He asked the teacher if he could go to the newspaper office in the town.

The teacher said that was a good idea. Elmer ran all the way. The editor of the newspaper listened. He watched Elmer sketch on paper a horse standing on a mountaintop. Then the editor took up the telephone. Elmer heard him talking to the engineer of the train.

"A newspaper has to check the facts," he said to Elmer. He made another call, this time long distance. "A story like this ought to make the city newspapers," he said. "Maybe even radio and TV."

"Thank you," Elmer said. "Do you think someone will know what to do?"

"We'll have to wait and see," the editor said. He picked up the picture Elmer had drawn of Lightning and turned away. Elmer went back to school.

The day seemed very long to Elmer. Late in the afternoon his teacher told him the principal would like to see him in the office.

When Elmer came through the office door, the principal smiled and handed him a newspaper.

There on the very front page was the picture Elmer had drawn. Underneath in big black print was: WHO WILL HELP LIGHTNING?

WHO WILL HELP LIGHTNING?

Elmer started to read the story printed below the picture. The principal turned on a small radio on the desk. A news commentator told about the trouble Lightning was in. Then he said, "Already this radio station has had offers from ranchers in the valley.

They will supply bales of hay and bags of grain if anyone knows a way of getting them to the mountaintop."

"Someone *will* know a way, don't you think, sir?" Elmer asked.

The principal looked grave. "I hope so," he said. "There will be news on TV in about ten minutes. Would you like to wait?"

School was out. Elmer could hear the boys and girls shout and run outside the building. He knew the train was waiting for him, but he stayed. The small TV set in a corner of the office was lighted. The principal turned the volume higher. A girl singer finished a blues song. A commercial told how to wash clothes whiter, brighter, sweeter. Elmer fidgeted on his chair. The engineer and fireman, waiting at the railroad station, would be impatient. But he *had* to know if anyone could help Lightning.

The picture on the TV screen changed. A news reporter sat at a desk. He spoke. With him was a tall young man wearing a uniform. "Captain Baker,"

the newsman
said. "I under-
stand you heard about
the horse on the mountaintop when we told the story earlier
on this station."

"That's right, sir," the young man said.

"And you came directly here," the newsman said.

23

"That's right, sir," the young man said. "I have a helicopter. I can drop hay and grain to the little horse."

The newsman was smiling his broadest grin right out into the room at Elmer. "I hope the boy who was responsible for telling this story to the public is listening in," he said. "I hope he is happy to know that Lightning will have food in a short time."

"I am! I am!" Elmer cried. He jumped right off the chair.

He thanked the principal and ran for his jacket. He ran all the way to the train. He told the engineer and fireman why he was late.

Usually that train could cross the divide in less than an hour. This afternoon it poked along and poked along, until Elmer and the engineer and the fireman heard a whir-whir overhead. They saw the helicopter circling. Then the train let out a whistle, whoo-woo-wo-o-ooo, and started for the top so fast that Elmer laughed. He knew, now, that the engineer and fireman had been wasting time. They

24

hoped the helicopter would come. They wanted to see it drop the bale of hay and bags of grain for Lightning.

The helicopter must have seen the train. It began

to follow along above the engine. It was growing dusk as they reached the top of the divide.

"Do you think the pilot will be able to find Lightning?" Elmer asked the engineer.

"We'll stop. The pilot will know this is the right place to look," the engineer said. He pushed in the throttle and put on the brake.

As the train waited, the helicopter began to circle. Nearer and nearer the flat top of the mountain it came. Elmer could see the bale of hay dangling from the small machine. The wind was strong on the top. It caught the helicopter. The helicopter slanted sideways. It dipped too fast. Elmer's heart beat hard.

The helicopter righted itself and began to circle again. The wind blew it this way and that. Again and again the helicopter tried to draw close enough to drop the hay. The food must fall in the right place or it would go over the boulder and be lost in the deep snow.

Elmer watched the little machine battle the wind.

He saw that this was a dangerous task. He was thankful to the pilot. He was thankful to the newspaper and radio and TV men. He was thankful to every person who worked hard to help a little horse.

The helicopter hovered closer and closer. Lightning raced about on the flat boulder. Then the hay fell beside her. She tossed her white mane and kicked up her black hind heels. She ran in a circle.

"Don't be afraid!" Elmer shouted. "It's hay!"

Maybe Lightning smelled the hay. She went over to it and began to eat. She ate as if she had never

tasted anything so good. She didn't even look up when the train started down the mountain to take Elmer home.

For three weeks the helicopter dropped hay and grain to feed Lightning. Then a warm spell came. The snow began to melt. The little horse found her way down to the track. When the train came by, Lightning saw Elmer in the window. She raced behind the train all the way to the construction camp where Elmer lived. Elmer got off the train and went up to Lightning, standing there. "Hello, Lightning," he said.

The little horse reached out with her nose and nuzzled Elmer's jacket. Then Lightning followed Elmer home.

The newspapers and the radio and the TV announcers told that the little horse had gone to Elmer's camp. Letters poured into the newspaper office and the stations.

Housewives and merchants said Elmer should keep Lightning. Elmer was the one who saved her.

He discovered her in trouble and asked for help.

Boys and girls wrote that Lightning wanted to stay with Elmer. She had followed him home.

Ranchers wrote that the little horse belonged to one of them. No one knew which one. She had been left behind, accidentally, when the horses were rounded up from the mountain pastures in the fall.

The ranchers agreed that Elmer should have her.

Elmer and his father built a warm stall for Lightning in the railroad train shed.

Each morning Lightning waits with Elmer for the train. On sunny days, she races beside the train. But if one flake of snow falls, Lightning kicks up her hind hoofs. She tosses her white mane. She runs to the

warm stall. She whinnies loud and sassy as if to say,
"No race today. I won't get into *that fix* again."
Now Elmer isn't lonely any more.